ORCHARD BOOKS
First published in Great Britain in 2018 by The Watts Publishing Group
1 3 5 7 9 10 8 6 4 2

A CIP catalogue record for this book is available from the British Library.

ISBN 978 1 40835 476 6

Printed and bound in China

FSC
www.fsc.org

MIX
Paper from
responsible sources
FSC® C104740

Orchard Books
An imprint of Hachette Children's Group
Part of The Watts Publishing Group Limited
Carmelite House
50 Victoria Embankment
London EC4Y 0DZ

An Hachette UK Company
www.hachette.co.uk

www.hachettechildrens.co.uk

THIS BOOK BELONGS TO

_____

TOOLS AND MATERIALS

BEFORE YOU START DRAWING YOU WILL NEED:

A pencil:
Use it to create the outline
of each character

Pencil sharpener:
Keep your pencil
nice and sharp

Eraser:
To erase
mistakes and
pencil lines from
final drawings

A blank pad:
A separate pad lets you
practise your drawings
over and over!

Coloured pencils:
Bring your characters
to life by adding colour.
You could also use
pens or paint – it's
up to you!

HOW TO USE THIS BOOK

Learn to draw Pokémon by following the simple steps in this book. You'll be amazed at how fun and easy drawing can be!

1

Start your drawings in the middle of the paper so you don't run out of space.

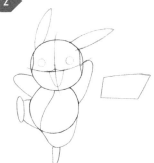

2

Each new step appears in blue, so draw all the blue lines you see.

3

Clean up the lines of your drawing and add the details.

4

Darken the lines you want to keep and erase the rest.

5

Add colour and shading to make your drawing really come alive!

BULBASAUR

Bulbasaur can be seen napping in bright sunlight. The seed on its back grows larger by soaking up the sun's rays.

CATEGORY: Seed
TYPE: Grass-Poison
HEIGHT: 0.7 m / 2'04"
WEIGHT: 6.9 kg / 15.2 lbs.

1

Start by drawing Bulbasaur's basic outline.

2

Add its seed, limbs and facial features.

3

Add detail to its skin, eyes and seed. Draw its claws.

4

Erase extra lines and go over Bulbasaur's outline.

Draw here!

CHARMANDER

The flame that burns at the tip of Charmander's tail shows its emotions. The flame flickers when Charmander is happy. If the Pokémon is angry, the flame burns more brightly.

CATEGORY: Lizard
TYPE: Fire
HEIGHT: 0.6 m / 2'00"
WEIGHT: 8.5 kg / 18.7 lbs.

1

Start with the outline of Charmander's head and body.

2

Add its limbs, eye details and all-important tail.

3

Add detail to its mouth, arms and legs. Add the flame.

4

Go over the final outline and erase unwanted lines.

Draw here!

SQUIRTLE

Squirtle's shell is not only for protection. The shell's rounded shape and grooves on the surface help reduce resistance in water. This Pokémon can swim very quickly underwater!

CATEGORY: Tiny Turtle
TYPE: Water
HEIGHT: 0.5 m / 1'08"
WEIGHT: 9.0 kg / 19.8 lbs.

1

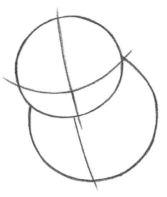

Draw two circles for Squirtle's head and body.

2

Add four limbs, an oval for the end of its tail and facial details.

3

Draw the grooves on Squirtle's shell and its eyes. Finish its tail.

4

Check the final details and erase any lines you don't need.

Draw here!

The forest is missing some Pokémon!
Add Bulbasaur, Charmander and Squirtle
then colour in the scene.

CHIKORITA

During battle, Chikorita waves its long leaf at opponents. The calming smell helps to keep enemies away.

CATEGORY: Leaf
TYPE: Grass
HEIGHT: 0.9 m / 2'11"
WEIGHT: 6.4 kg / 14.1 lbs.

1

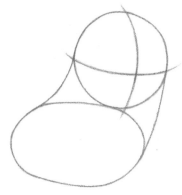

A circle and oval form the basic shape of Chikorita.

2

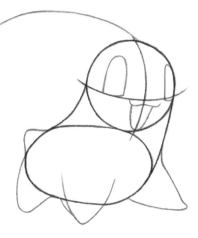

Add the outlines of its limbs and draw the basic shape of the leaf.

3

Finish Chikorita's leaf and add detail to its face and body.

4

Erase extra lines and add any finishing touches.

Draw here!

CYNDAQUIL

Cyndaquil uses the flames on its back to protect itself.
When Cyndaquil is tired the flames are weaker
but when it's angry they burn high and hot!

CATEGORY:
Fire Mouse
TYPE: Fire
HEIGHT: 0.5 m / 1'08"
WEIGHT:
7.9 kg / 17.4 lbs.

1

Draw the basic lines of
Cyndaquil and the small flames.

2

Add shape to its nose and limbs.
Extend the flames on its back.

3

Add details to Cyndaquil's face and body. Add the final flames.

4

Erase any extra lines, make sure its flames are burning brightly!

Draw here!

TOTODILE

Totodile may look cute but watch out! Its jaws are
so powerful they can cause serious injury
even when playing.

CATEGORY: Big Jaw
TYPE: Water
HEIGHT: 0.6 m / 2'00"
WEIGHT:
9.5 kg / 20.9 lbs.

1

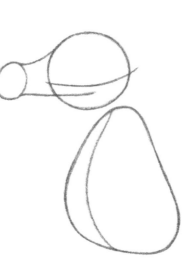

Begin by outlining the head,
long nose and body of Totodile.

2

Start to add the details
to the face and body.

3

Draw eyes, teeth, spikes and body markings.

4

Erase the outlines and go over the finishing details.

Draw here!

Chikorita, Cyndaquil and Totodile are meeting by the river.
Draw them in the scene and then colour it in.

TREECKO

Treecko is cool, calm and collected. If a bigger Pokémon glares at Treecko, it will stand its ground without panicking.

CATEGORY: Wood Gecko
TYPE: Grass
HEIGHT: 0.5 m / 1'08"
WEIGHT: 5.0 kg / 11.0 lbs.

1

Two oval shapes form the basis of Treecko.

2

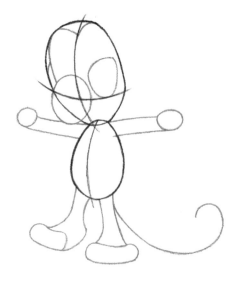

Add the limbs, the beginning of the tail and facial features.

3

Finish the tail and add detail to the body and eyes.

4

Erase the guidelines and touch up any details.

Draw here!

TORCHIC

Torchic's internal fire and soft feathers make it perfect for cuddling! In battle, it can breathe flames and shoot fireballs!

CATEGORY: Chick
TYPE: Fire
HEIGHT: 0.4 m / 1'04"
WEIGHT: 2.5 kg / 5.5 lbs.

1

Draw an oval for the head and the basic body shape.

2

Add its feathers, facial features, body feathers and legs.

3

Add the final details to Torchic, taking care over its feathers.

4

Erase the outlines from Torchic and go over the final lines.

Draw here!

MUDKIP

Mudkip breathes through the gills on its cheeks. Its fin is so sensitive to the motion of air and water it can sense movement with its eyes closed.

CATEGORY: Mud Fish
TYPE: Water
HEIGHT: 0.4 m / 1'04"
WEIGHT:
7.6 kg / 16.8 lbs.

1

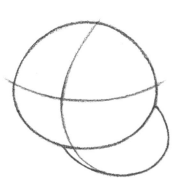

Draw Mudkip's head and basic body shape.

2

Add legs and draw the detail of Mudkip's face.

3

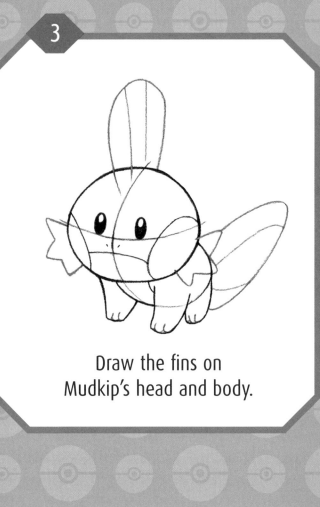

Draw the fins on
Mudkip's head and body.

4

Add the finishing touches and
erase unwanted outlines.

Draw here!

Journey into the forest with Treecko, Torchic and Mudkip.
Draw them in the scene and then add lots of colour.

TURTWIG

Turtwig's shell is made out of soil! If it doesn't drink enough water its leaves will wilt.

CATEGORY:
Tiny Leaf
TYPE: Grass
HEIGHT: 0.4 m / 1'04"
WEIGHT:
10.2 kg / 22.5 lbs.

1

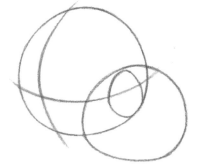

Draw the three basic shapes that are the basis of Turtwig.

2

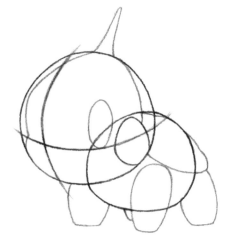

Draw the leg shapes and add detail to the head and body.

3

Draw the leaves, finish the eye and define its shell.

4

Check all final details before erasing leftover guidelines.

Draw here!

CHIMCHAR

Chimchar is always on fire – even when it rains!
If it's not feeling well, the flame flickers weakly.

CATEGORY: Chimp
TYPE: Fire
HEIGHT: 0.5 m / 1'08"
WEIGHT:
6.2 kg / 13.7 lbs.

1

A circle and pear-shape are
the basis of Chimchar.

2

Draw the basic outlines of all
four limbs and eye shapes.

3

Add detail to Chimchar's face and body – don't forget the fiery tail!

4

Retrace final lines and erase any unwanted guides.

Draw here!

PIPLUP

Piplup is stubborn and can be a challenge to train.
It's quite independent and prefers to find its own food.

CATEGORY: Penguin
TYPE: Water
HEIGHT: 0.4 m / 1'04"
WEIGHT:
5.2 kg / 11.5 lbs.

1

Draw the basic outline and facial
feature placement lines.

2

Add Piplup's beak and eye
then add detail to the body.

3

Draw face and body
markings and add the tail.

4

Erase the guidelines
to finish Piplup.

Draw here!

Draw Turtwig, Chimchar and Piplup together in the mountains. Then finish the scene by colouring it in!

SNIVY

If it's sunny, Snivy can soak up sunlight with its
tail – this makes it a much faster runner!

CATEGORY:
Grass Snake
TYPE: Grass
HEIGHT: 0.6 m / 2'00"
WEIGHT:
8.1 kg / 17.9 lbs.

1

Draw a circle for the head and
two curved lines for the body.

2

Two more lines complete the
head then add limbs and tail fan.

3

Draw detail in Snivy's eye, finish
the tail fan and add its ruff.

4

Erase any unwanted lines
and check all body details.

Draw here!

TEPIG

Tepig uses the fireballs from its nose in battle – and in cooking! It likes to roast berries though sometimes they can be a little overdone.

CATEGORY: Fire Pig
TYPE: Fire
HEIGHT: 0.5 m / 1'08"
WEIGHT:
9.9 kg / 21.8 lbs.

1

Draw the basic outline of Tepig's head and body.

2

Add eye, mouth and nose outlines, limbs and the tail.

3

Connect the tail, add the
ears and final facial details.

4

Erase the guidelines and
add any final details.

Draw here!

OSHAWOTT

Oshawott can detach the shell on its belly, called
a scalchop, and use it as a weapon in battle.

CATEGORY:
Sea Otter
TYPE: Water
HEIGHT: 0.5 m / 1'08"
WEIGHT:
5.9 kg / 13.0 lbs.

1

Draw the outlines of
Oshawott's head and body.

2

Draw the basic eyes, nose,
mouth, limbs and scalchop.

3

Add detail to the face and body, and draw the tail.

4

Erase the guidelines, taking care where the head and body meet.

Draw here!

PIKACHU

Pikachu stores electricity in its cheeks to use when it gets angry. It sometimes uses this electricity to recharge other Pikachu that have been weakened.

CATEGORY: Mouse
TYPE: Electric
HEIGHT: 0.4 m / 1'04"
WEIGHT: 6.0 kg / 13.2 lbs.

1

Draw two circles as the basis for Pikachu.

2

Flesh out Pikachu's body, add the ears and end of the tail.

3

Add detail to the face and ears and attach the tail to the body.

4

Erase the remaining guidelines to finish Pikachu.

Draw here!

Draw Snivy, Tepig, Oshawott and Pikachu having fun by the river. Then colour in the bright scene.

CHESPIN

Chespin's soft quills can become tough spikes. Its nut-like shell provides extra protection against enemies.

CATEGORY: Spiny Nut
TYPE: Grass
HEIGHT: 0.4 m / 1'04"
WEIGHT: 9.0 kg / 19.8 lbs.

1

Draw the outline of Chespin's head and body.

2

Add the limbs, facial features and quills on its head.

3

Add detail to Chespin's face, then the final quills and tail.

4

Erase any extra guidelines and finish Chespin.

Draw here!

FENNEKIN

Eating twigs gives Fennekin energy! Extreme heat from its ears keeps enemies at a distance.

CATEGORY: Fox
TYPE: Fire
HEIGHT: 0.4 m / 1'04"
WEIGHT: 9.4 kg / 20.7 lbs.

1

Draw the basic outline of Fennekin, including the big ears.

2

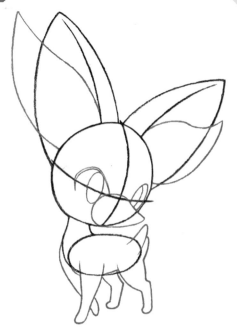

Add four limbs, facial outlines and basic flame-like details.

3

Finish Fennekin's tail,
fur and flame-like details.

4

Erase the final guidelines
and add any final details.

Draw here!

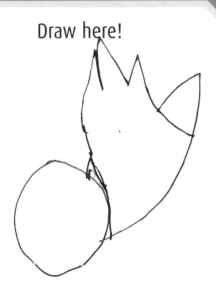

FROAKIE

Foamy bubbles on Froakie protect its sensitive skin.
It's always on high alert for any danger close to it.

CATEGORY:
Bubble Frog
TYPE: Water
HEIGHT: 0.3 m / 1'00"
WEIGHT:
7.0 kg / 15.4 lbs.

1

Draw an oval for Froakie's
head, body and two big eyes.

2

Add the back and front legs,
eyes, nose and mouth line.

3

Draw the detail of the eyes and foamy bubbles on Froakie's skin.

4

Erase the extra lines and check all Froakie's details.

Draw here!

This open field is perfect for Pokémon. Draw Chespin,
Fennekin and Froakie in the scene and then colour it in.

ROWLET

During night-time Rowlet flies silently, sneaking up on other Pokémon and launching fierce kicking attacks.

CATEGORY: Grass Quill
TYPE: Grass-Flying
HEIGHT: 0.3 m / 1'0"
WEIGHT: 1.5 kg / 3.3 lbs.

1

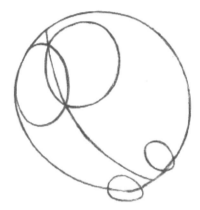

Five differently sized circles form the basis of Rowlet.

2

Add three long ovals for Rowlet's wings and add body detail.

3

Add the eyes, beak,
claws and feather details.

4

Trace over Rowlet and
add any final details.

Draw here!

LITTEN

Litten's flaming fur can be used in fiery attacks on enemies.
Trainers find it difficult to get this Pokémon to trust them.

CATEGORY: Fire Cat
TYPE: Fire
HEIGHT: 0.4 m / 1'04"
WEIGHT:
4.3 kg / 9.4 lbs.

1

Draw the outline of Litten's
head, body and ears.

2

Add the limbs, basic eye
shape, ear detail and the tail.

3

Draw Litten's facial fur and markings on its head and body.

4

Erase the guidelines and finish Litten.

Draw here!

POPPLIO

Popplio practises blowing water balloons from its nose.
It uses these balloons as a weapon in battle!

CATEGORY: Sea Lion
TYPE: Water
HEIGHT: 0.4 m / 1'04"
WEIGHT:
7.5 kg / 16.5 lbs.

1

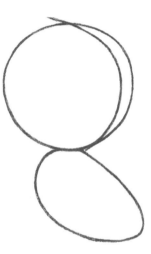

Draw the outline of
Popplio's head and body.

2

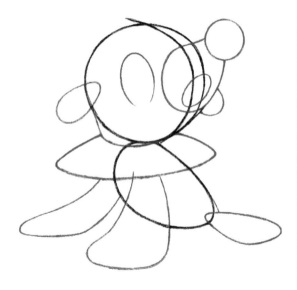

Add the shape to Popplio's
head and its flippers.

3

Draw eye and mouth details
and the shape of the ruff.

4

Retrace over the final lines and
erase any unwanted guides.

Draw here!

Draw Rowlet, Litten and Popplio in this scene,
then add lots of colour to bring them to life!

DON'T MISS THESE OTHER OFFICIAL POKÉMON BOOKS